OFFICIAL SQA PAST PAPERS WITH ANSWERS

INTERMEDIATE 2 | UNITS 1, 2 & APPLICATIONS

MATHEMATICS
2009-2013

HODDER GIBSON
LEARN MORE

SQA

Hachette UK's policy is to use papers that are natural, renewable and recyclable products and made from wood grown in sustainable forests. The logging and manufacturing processes are expected to conform to the environmental regulations of the country of origin.

Orders: please contact Bookpoint Ltd, 130 Park Drive, Abingdon, Oxon OX14 4SE. Telephone: (44) 01235 827720. Fax: (44) 01235 400454.

Lines are open 9.00–5.00, Monday to Saturday, with a 24-hour message answering service. Visit our website at www.hoddereducation.co.uk. Hodder Gibson can be contacted direct on: Tel: 0141 848 1609; Fax: 0141 889 6315; email: hoddergibson@hodder.co.uk

This collection first published in 2013 by

Hodder Gibson, an imprint of Hodder Education,

An Hachette UK Company

2a Christie Street

Paisley PA1 1NB

BrightRED   Hodder Gibson is grateful to Bright Red Publishing Ltd for collaborative work in preparation of this book and all PUBLISHING   SQA Past Paper and National 5 Model Paper titles 2013.

Typeset by PDQ Digital Media Solutions Ltd, Bungay, Suffolk NR35 1BY

Printed in the UK

A catalogue record for this title is available from the British Library

ISBN 978-1-4718-0259-1

3 2 1

2014 2013

Introduction

Study Skills – what you need to know to pass exams!

Pause for thought

Many students might skip quickly through a page like this. After all, we all know how to revise. Do you really though?

Think about this:

"IF YOU ALWAYS DO WHAT YOU ALWAYS DO, YOU WILL ALWAYS GET WHAT YOU HAVE ALWAYS GOT."

Do you like the grades you get? Do you want to do better? If you get full marks in your assessment, then that's great! Change nothing! This section is just to help you get that little bit better than you already are.

There are two main parts to the advice on offer here. The first part highlights fairly obvious things but which are also very important. The second part makes suggestions about revision that you might not have thought about but which WILL help you.

Part 1

DOH! It's so obvious but …

Start revising in good time

Don't leave it until the last minute – this will make you panic.

Make a revision timetable that sets out work time AND play time.

Sleep and eat!

Obvious really, and very helpful. Avoid arguments or stressful things too – even games that wind you up. You need to be fit, awake and focused!

Know your place!

Make sure you know exactly **WHEN and WHERE** your exams are.

Know your enemy!

Make sure you know what to expect in the exam.

How is the paper structured?

How much time is there for each question?

What types of question are involved?

Which topics seem to come up time and time again?

Which topics are your strongest and which are your weakest?

Are all topics compulsory or are there choices?

Learn by DOING!

There is no substitute for past papers and practice papers – they are simply essential! Tackling this collection of papers and answers is exactly the right thing to be doing as your exams approach.

Part 2

People learn in different ways. Some like low light, some bright. Some like early morning, some like evening / night. Some prefer warm, some prefer cold. But everyone uses their BRAIN and the brain works when it is active. Passive learning – sitting gazing at notes – is the most INEFFICIENT way to learn anything. Below you will find tips and ideas for making your revision more effective and maybe even more enjoyable. What follows gets your brain active, and active learning works!

Activity 1 – Stop and review

Step 1

When you have done no more than 5 minutes of revision reading STOP!

Step 2

Write a heading in your own words which sums up the topic you have been revising.

Step 3

Write a summary of what you have revised in no more than two sentences. Don't fool yourself by saying, 'I know it but I cannot put it into words'. That just means you don't know it well enough. If you cannot write your summary, revise that section again, knowing that you must write a summary at the end of it. Many of you will have notebooks full of blue/black ink writing. Many of the pages will not be especially attractive or memorable so try to liven them up a bit with colour as you are reviewing and rewriting. **This is a great memory aid, and memory is the most important thing.**

Activity 2 — Use technology!

Why should everything be written down? Have you thought about 'mental' maps, diagrams, cartoons and colour to help you learn? And rather than write down notes, why not record your revision material?

What about having a text message revision session with friends? Keep in touch with them to find out how and what they are revising and share ideas and questions.

Why not make a video diary where you tell the camera what you are doing, what you think you have learned and what you still have to do? No one has to see or hear it but the process of having to organise your thoughts in a formal way to explain something is a very important learning practice.

Be sure to make use of electronic files. You could begin to summarise your class notes. Your typing might be slow but it will get faster and the typed notes will be easier to read than the scribbles in your class notes. Try to add different fonts and colours to make your work stand out. You can easily Google relevant pictures, cartoons and diagrams which you can copy and paste to make your work more attractive and **MEMORABLE**.

Activity 3 – This is it. Do this and you will know lots!

Step 1

In this task you must be very honest with yourself! Find the SQA syllabus for your subject (www.sqa.org.uk). Look at how it is broken down into main topics called MANDATORY knowledge. That means stuff you MUST know.

Step 2

BEFORE you do ANY revision on this topic, write a list of everything that you already know about the subject. It might be quite a long list but you only need to write it once. It shows you all the information that is already in your long-term memory so you know what parts you do not need to revise!

Step 3

Pick a chapter or section from your book or revision notes. Choose a fairly large section or a whole chapter to get the most out of this activity.

With a buddy, use Skype, Facetime, Twitter or any other communication you have, to play the game "If this is the answer, what is the question?". For example, if you are revising Geography and the answer you provide is "meander", your buddy would have to make up a question like "What is the word that describes a feature of a river where it flows slowly and bends often from side to side?".

Make up 10 "answers" based on the content of the chapter or section you are using. Give this to your buddy to solve while you solve theirs.

Step 4

Construct a wordsearch of at least 10 X 10 squares. You can make it as big as you like but keep it realistic. Work together with a group of friends. Many apps allow you to make wordsearch puzzles online. The words and phrases can go in any direction and phrases can be split. Your puzzle must only contain facts linked to the topic you are revising. Your task is to find 10 bits of information to hide in your puzzle but you must not repeat information that you used in Step 3. DO NOT show where the words are. Fill up empty squares with random letters. Remember to keep a note of where your answers are hidden but do not show your friends. When you have a complete puzzle, exchange it with a friend to solve each other's puzzle.

Step 5

Now make up 10 questions (not "answers" this time) based on the same chapter used in the previous two tasks. Again, you must find NEW information that you have not yet used. Now it's getting hard to find that new information! Again, give your questions to a friend to answer.

Step 6

As you have been doing the puzzles, your brain has been actively searching for new information. Now write a NEW LIST that contains only the new information you have discovered when doing the puzzles. Your new list is the one to look at repeatedly for short bursts over the next few days. Try to remember more and more of it without looking at it. After a few days, you should be able to add words from your second list to your first list as you increase the information in your long-term memory.

FINALLY! Be inspired...

Make a list of different revision ideas and beside each one write **THINGS I HAVE** tried, **THINGS I WILL** try and **THINGS I MIGHT** try. Don't be scared of trying something new.

And remember – "FAIL TO PREPARE AND PREPARE TO FAIL!"

Intermediate 2 Mathematics Units 1, 2 and Applications

The course

Intermediate 2 Mathematics is divided into 3 units. Unit 1 is subdivided into five outcomes (appreciation, volume, straight line, breaking brackets / factorisation and circle work). Unit 2 has four outcomes (trigonometry, simultaneous equations, graphs / charts and statistics). The Applications Unit has four outcomes (social topics, logic diagrams and spreadsheets, formulae, and more statistics). The Course Arrangements can be accessed and downloaded from the SQA webpage http://www.sqa.org.uk/sqa/39090.html and give more detail on the course content.

Your task is to develop your knowledge of these outcomes and the skills necessary to deal with them and also to demonstrate your understanding by applying this knowledge and these skills correctly and appropriately.

How the course is graded

The grade you finally get for Intermediate 2 Mathematics depends on two things:

- the internal assessments you do in school or college (the "NABs") – these don't count towards the final grade, but you must have passed them before you can achieve a final award. It is worth noting here that the "NABs" are set at 'minimum competence', i.e. the final examination will be harder and more complex than the "NABs".

- the two exam papers you sit in May – that's what this book is all about!

The exams

Paper 1 lasts for 45 minutes, is worth 30 marks and must be completed without the aid of a calculator.

Paper 2 lasts for 1 hour 30 minutes, is worth 50 marks and a calculator can be used in this paper.

Remember that in both papers there will be a page of formulae that you will find useful. Don't forget to use it!

The papers are designed to contain around 35% of 'non-routine' material, i.e. questions where the strategy may not be obvious and you may have to think a bit about how to tackle them. Also 35% of the papers will consist of more difficult questions, e.g. given the volume of a shape, calculate its height.

Areas of strength and weakness

In 2012, over 23 000 candidates were presented for Intermediate 2 Mathematics. Across a large number like this it is easy to spot topics which have been done well and also topics where common errors appear.

Where candidates get it right

In general, candidates seem to be more successful in dealing with the material in **Units 1 and 2**. For example, questions on appreciation/depreciation (e.g. 2011, Paper 2 Q2), volume (e.g. 2012, Paper 2 Q3), finding the equation of a straight line (e.g. 2010, Paper 1 Q1), breaking brackets (e.g. 2011, Paper 1 Q2), finding the length of an arc or area of a segment (e.g. 2011, Paper 2 Q5) all seem to be well done. As do basic trigonometric calculations (e.g. 2008, Paper 1 Q6), simultaneous equations (e.g. 2010, Paper 2 Q5), and statistics (2010, Paper 1 Q2 or 2009, Paper 2 Q2).

Where candidates have difficulty

Some topics in the Applications Unit consistently seem to cause difficulty for candidates, e.g. using a credit card and spreadsheets, even when these questions are fairly straightforward. In the spreadsheet questions the candidates can work out values for the cells correctly but often fail to write the formula correctly. Remember for spreadsheets, all formulae **must** begin with an equals sign. Also multiplication is represented by an asterisk (*) and division by an oblique sign (/). So to represent a formula where cell B10 is multiplied by 1.025 and divided by 12 we would write =B10*1.025/12.

How to improve your marks

Although material from Units 1 and 2 tends to be tackled more successfully by candidates, when a question is slightly different from those in previous years there can be a disproportionate drop in marks awarded. For example, in 2012, Paper 1 Q3 was a question on the Straight Line but was different from the normal *"Find the equation of the given line"*. Consequently many candidates did not perform well in this question. You must be prepared to tackle **'non-routine' questions**: they will make up roughly 35% of the total question paper.

No calculator in Paper 1!

Paper 1 has to be tackled without the use of a calculator. In previous years topics which have been tested in Paper 1 include calculating volume (2010, Paper 1 Q3), area of a triangle, using trig formula (2012, Paper 1 Q7) and standard deviation (2007, Paper 1 Q6). These are all topics which appear more commonly in Paper 2. Because they are in Paper 1, the setters will have chosen the figures carefully so that the calculations do not become too unwieldy. Usually, re-ordering the numbers, or 'cancelling' fractions will ease calculations.

Showing working

On the cover of the examination paper, candidates are instructed to **show all working**. This is a very important part of scoring well in the examination. **For all questions worth more than 1 mark, evidence of a method must be shown.** It is especially critical for questions worth 4 or 5 marks. Sometimes for these questions, 4 out of 5 marks are for correct strategies and only 1 mark for correct calculations. So even if you make a mistake in the calculation and arrive at the wrong answer, it may be possible to receive up to 4 out of 5 marks for tackling the problem in an appropriate way. So it is vital that the marker can clearly see the strategy you are following! This would apply in trigonometry questions such as 2010 Paper 2 Q12. Detailed Marking Instructions are available from the SQA website http://www.sqa.org.uk/sqa/39090.html and these are useful in showing how marks are awarded and what evidence is expected / acceptable.

Communicating strategies

Candidates sometimes find it difficult to **communicate** the strategies being used. They show all their calculations but, where the question is a complex one, it may be difficult for the marker to see what the numbers in the calculations are referring to. In cases like this it is often very helpful to use a **diagram** to convey information to enable the marker to understand the strategy you are using. In 2012, Paper 1 Q4 (Angles in a circle) and Paper 2 Q12 (complex trig problem) were questions in this category. If you are able to mark sizes of lines and angles on to a diagram in your response, you will make it easier for the markers to follow the strategy and to award marks.

Complex trig questions

Complex trig questions are usually worth around 5 marks. Where you see a question like this, try to establish how many triangles are in the diagram and even draw them out separately to enable you to decide on the sizes of sides and angles known in each triangle. Where 5 marks are being awarded for a trig question, it usually means you have to work in 2 different triangles, finding a missing size in one and then using it in a different triangle to find the size asked for in the question.

Statistics questions

Statistics questions are usually very well done. The exception to this is the *interpretation* of statistics, usually tested in part (b) of a question. Generally candidates will be asked to comment on how two sets of statistics compare, using measures of average (median, mean) and/or measures of spread (semi-interquartile range, standard deviation).

However it is not enough to say that one standard deviation is greater or smaller than the other. Comparisons must be made in context to show some understanding of what the information is telling us. Some candidates have difficulty in explaining the comparisons. In 2012, Paper 2 Q5, candidates performed better than usual, probably because a choice of statements had been given and candidates had simply to pick the appropriate ones. Usually candidates have to devise the form of words in which to express the answer. Again the Detailed Marking Instructions on the SQA website will offer you the various acceptable answers for this type of question.

Be systematic!

A systematic approach is always best. Be sure to download the Arrangements Documents from the SQA website so that you have a checklist for the course content and can be certain you have covered all aspects of the course. Use this book to tackle as many specific topics in past papers as you can! For example, if you want to focus on questions to do with percentage appreciation or depreciation then try all those questions that you can find (there will usually be one per year). If you are stuck on a particular question, get someone to explain how to do it, then **try it by yourself**. Come back to it again at a later date and try it again. Keep a record of the questions you have tried (maybe a tick beside it if you solve it by yourself and a question mark if you have to come back to it again). When you have completed the course then you can try **whole** past papers to check your timing. Older papers are available on the SQA website if you would like a change!

Good luck!

Remember that the rewards for passing Intermediate 2 Mathematics are well worth it! Your pass will help you get the future you want for yourself. In the exam, be confident in your own ability, if you're not sure how to answer a question trust your instincts and just give it a go anyway – keep calm and don't panic! GOOD LUCK!

INTERMEDIATE 2

2009

[BLANK PAGE]

X101/202

NATIONAL
QUALIFICATIONS
2009

THURSDAY, 21 MAY
1.00 PM – 1.45 PM

MATHEMATICS
INTERMEDIATE 2
Units 1, 2 and
Applications of Mathematics
Paper 1
(Non-calculator)

Read carefully

1   **You may NOT use a calculator.**

2   Full credit will be given only where the solution contains appropriate working.

3   Square-ruled paper is provided.

FORMULAE LIST

Sine rule: $\dfrac{a}{\sin A} = \dfrac{b}{\sin B} = \dfrac{c}{\sin C}$

Cosine rule: $a^2 = b^2 + c^2 - 2bc \cos A$ or $\cos A = \dfrac{b^2 + c^2 - a^2}{2bc}$

Area of a triangle: Area $= \frac{1}{2} ab \sin C$

Volume of a sphere: Volume $= \frac{4}{3}\pi r^3$

Volume of a cone: Volume $= \frac{1}{3}\pi r^2 h$

Volume of a cylinder: Volume $= \pi r^2 h$

Standard deviation: $s = \sqrt{\dfrac{\sum(x - \bar{x})^2}{n-1}} = \sqrt{\dfrac{\sum x^2 - (\sum x)^2 / n}{n-1}}$, where n is the sample size.

Marks

ALL questions should be attempted.

1. The number of goals scored one weekend by each team in the Football League is shown below.

0	1	1	2	1	0	0	5	0	1	3
0	2	2	1	1	3	0	0	2	4	1

   (*a*) Construct a dotplot for the data.   **2**

   (*b*) The shape of the distribution is

          A   skewed to the right
          B   symmetric
          C   skewed to the left
          D   uniform.

    Write down the letter that corresponds to the correct shape.   **1**

2.

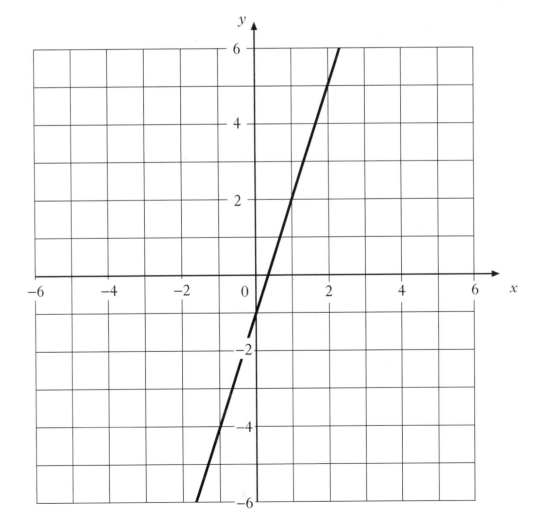

    Find the equation of the straight line shown in the diagram.   **3**

Marks

3. Factorise

$$x^2 - 5x - 24.$$

2

4. Multiply out the brackets and collect like terms.

$$(x + 5)(2x^2 - 3x - 1)$$

3

5. (*a*) The marks of a group of students in their October test are listed below.

41   56   68   59   43   37   70   58   61   47   75   66

Calculate:

(i)   the median;

1

(ii)   the semi-interquartile range.

3

(*b*) The teacher arranges extra homework classes for the students before the next test in December.

In this test, the median is 67 and the semi-interquartile range is 7.

Make **two** appropriate comments comparing the marks in the October and December tests.

2

6. An angle, $a°$, can be described by the following statements.

- a is greater than 0 and less than 360
- $\sin a°$ is negative
- $\cos a°$ is positive
- $\tan a°$ is negative

Write down a possible value for a.

1

7. A straight line is represented by the equation $x + y = 5$.
Find the gradient of this line.

2

Marks

8. Five towns are represented by letters A, B, C, D and E in the tree diagram shown below.

   The tree diagram represents routes between these five towns.

   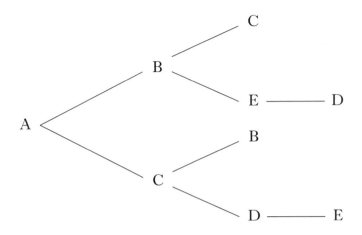

   Draw a network diagram to represent the routes shown in the tree diagram.   **2**

9. A company of window fitters uses a spreadsheet to show examples of how their prices are calculated.

	A	B	C	D	E
1	**Wendy's Window Fitters**		**Quotation for fitting windows**		
2	**VAT rate (%)**	17.5			
3					
4	**Window Size**	**Cost per window**	**Quantity of windows**	**Cost**	**Cost including VAT**
5					
6	30 cm by 30 cm	£50	3	£150	£176.25
7	50 cm by 70 cm	£75	4	£300	£352.50
8	120 cm by 100 cm	£120	2	£240	£282.00
9	90 cm by 150 cm	£125	1	£125	£146.88
10					
11					£957.63
12					

   (a) Write down the formula used in cell E11.   **1**

   (b) The VAT rate in cell B2 is changed.

   As a result, the values in column E are updated automatically.

   Write down the formula used in cell E6.   **2**

[Turn over for Question 10 on *Page six*

Marks

10. A three-dimensional solid is shown in the diagram below.

All dimensions are in centimetres.

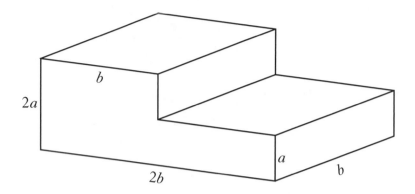

The surface area, S square centimetres, of this solid is given by the formula

$$S = 10ab + 4b^2.$$

(a) Calculate S when $a = 12$ and $b = 5$.   **2**

(b) Calculate a when $S = 424$ and $b = 4$.   **3**

[END OF QUESTION PAPER]

X101/204

NATIONAL
QUALIFICATIONS
2009

THURSDAY, 21 MAY
2.05 PM – 3.35 PM

MATHEMATICS
INTERMEDIATE 2
Units 1, 2 and
Applications of Mathematics
Paper 2

Read carefully

1   **Calculators may be used in this paper.**

2   Full credit will be given only where the solution contains appropriate working.

3   Square-ruled paper is provided.

FORMULAE LIST

Sine rule: $\dfrac{a}{\sin A} = \dfrac{b}{\sin B} = \dfrac{c}{\sin C}$

Cosine rule: $a^2 = b^2 + c^2 - 2bc \cos A$ or $\cos A = \dfrac{b^2 + c^2 - a^2}{2bc}$

Area of a triangle: Area $= \frac{1}{2} ab \sin C$

Volume of a sphere: Volume $= \frac{4}{3} \pi r^3$

Volume of a cone: Volume $= \frac{1}{3} \pi r^2 h$

Volume of a cylinder: Volume $= \pi r^2 h$

Standard deviation: $s = \sqrt{\dfrac{\sum (x - \bar{x})^2}{n-1}} = \sqrt{\dfrac{\sum x^2 - (\sum x)^2 / n}{n-1}}$, where n is the sample size.

ALL questions should be attempted.

Marks

1. A new book "Intermediate 2 Maths is Fun" was published in 2006.
   There were 3000 sales of the book during that year.
   Sales rose by 11% in 2007 then fell by 10% in 2008.

   Were the sales in 2008 more or less than the sales in 2006?

   You must give a reason for your answer.   3

2. The heights, in centimetres, of seven netball players are given below.

   173   176   168   166   170   180   171

   For this sample, calculate:

   (*a*) the mean;   1

   (*b*) the standard deviation.   3

   Show clearly all your working.

                                                              [Turn over

Marks

3. A company manufactures aluminium tubes.

    The cross-section of one of the tubes is shown in the diagram below.

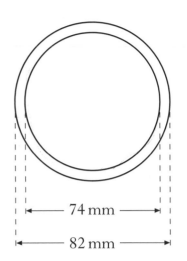 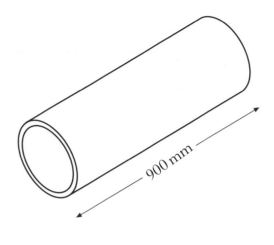

    The inner diameter is 74 millimetres.

    The outer diameter is 82 millimetres.

    The tube is 900 millimetres long.

    Calculate the volume of aluminium used to make the tube.

    Give your answer correct to three significant figures.   5

4. There are 14 cars and 60 passengers on the morning crossing of the ferry from Wemyss Bay to Rothesay. The total takings are £344·30.

    (*a*) Let x pounds be the cost for a car and y pounds be the cost for a passenger.

    Write down an equation in x and y which satisfies the above condition.   1

    (*b*) There are 21 cars and 40 passengers on the evening crossing of the ferry. The total takings are £368·95.

    Write down a second equation in x and y which satisfies this condition.   1

    (*c*) Find the cost for a car and the cost for a passenger on the ferry.   4

Marks

5. A pet shop manufactures protective dog collars.

In the diagram below the shaded area represents one of these collars.

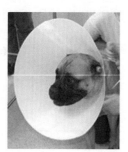

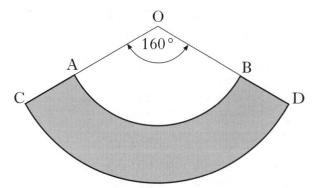

AB and CD are arcs of the circles with centres at O.

The radius, OA, is 10 inches and the radius, OC, is 18 inches.

Angle AOB is 160°.

Calculate the area of a collar.

4

6. The Bermuda triangle is an area in the Atlantic Ocean where many planes and ships have mysteriously disappeared.

Its vertices are at Bermuda (B), Miami (M) and Puerto Rico (P).

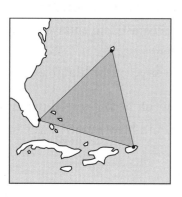

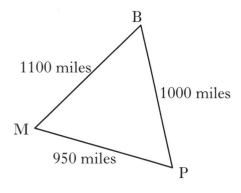

Calculate the size of angle BPM.

3

[Turn over

Marks

7. The table shown below is used to calculate loan repayments.

		60 months	48 months	24 months
		Monthly repayment (£)	Monthly repayment (£)	Monthly repayment (£)
With payment protection	£20 000	463·85	551·43	994·23
	£15 000	347·89	413·57	745·67
	£7500	173·94	206·79	372·84
Without payment protection	£20 000	384·65	467·72	884·47
	£15 000	288·49	350·79	663·35
	£7500	144·24	175·40	331·68

Samir wishes to borrow £15 000.

How much will the loan cost him if he repays it over 48 months, with payment protection? **3**

8. Jamie works as a potter for a company which makes china ornaments.

He earns a basic salary of £218 per week plus 80 pence for every ornament he makes.

Jamie saves $\frac{2}{5}$ of his gross pay every week.

One week he makes 40 ornaments.

Calculate how much Jamie saves that week. **3**

9. Anna earns £42 000 per year. She has tax allowances of £5425.

The rates of tax applicable for the year are given in the table below.

Taxable income (£)	Rate
On the first £34 600	20%
On any income over £34 600	40%

How much is Anna's **monthly** tax bill? **5**

Marks

10. For reasons of safety, a building is supported by two wooden struts, represented by DB and DC in the diagram below.

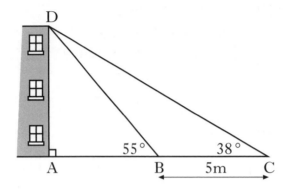

Angle ABD = 55°.

Angle BCD = 38°.

BC is 5 metres.

Calculate the height of the building represented by AD. 5

11. A railway goes through an underground tunnel.

The diagram below shows the cross-section of the tunnel. It consists of part of a circle with a horizontal base.

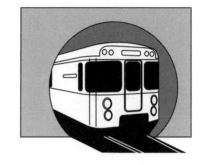

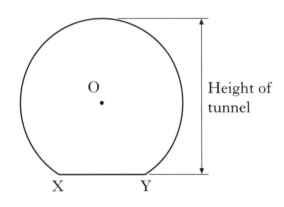

- The centre of the circle is O.
- XY is a chord of the circle.
- XY is 1·8 metres.
- The radius of the circle is 1·7 metres.

Find the height of the tunnel. 4

[Turn over for Question 12 on *Page eight*

Marks

12. The amount of money spent by each pupil in a school tuck shop is recorded.

The data collected is shown in the table below.

Amount spent (pence)	Frequency
1– 50	42
51–100	64
101–150	35
151–200	18
201–250	12
251–300	10

Calculate the mean amount of money spent by pupils in the tuck shop.   **5**

[END OF QUESTION PAPER]

[BLANK PAGE]

X101/202

NATIONAL
QUALIFICATIONS
2010

FRIDAY, 21 MAY
1.00 PM – 1.45 PM

MATHEMATICS
INTERMEDIATE 2
Units 1, 2 and
Applications of Mathematics
Paper 1
(Non-calculator)

Read carefully

1 **You may NOT use a calculator.**

2 Full credit will be given only where the solution contains appropriate working.

3 Square-ruled paper is provided.

FORMULAE LIST

Sine rule: $\dfrac{a}{\sin A} = \dfrac{b}{\sin B} = \dfrac{c}{\sin C}$

Cosine rule: $a^2 = b^2 + c^2 - 2bc \cos A$ or $\cos A = \dfrac{b^2 + c^2 - a^2}{2bc}$

Area of a triangle: $\text{Area} = \frac{1}{2} ab \sin C$

Volume of a sphere: $\text{Volume} = \frac{4}{3} \pi r^3$

Volume of a cone: $\text{Volume} = \frac{1}{3} \pi r^2 h$

Volume of a cylinder: $\text{Volume} = \pi r^2 h$

Standard deviation: $s = \sqrt{\dfrac{\sum (x - \bar{x})^2}{n-1}} = \sqrt{\dfrac{\sum x^2 - (\sum x)^2 / n}{n-1}}$, where n is the sample size.

Marks

ALL questions should be attempted.

1.

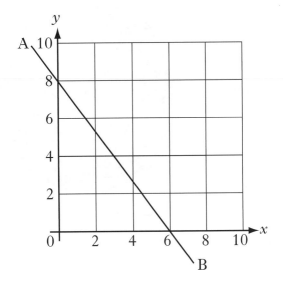

Find the equation of the straight line AB shown in the diagram. 3

2. The pupils in a primary class record their shoe sizes as shown below.

$$
\begin{array}{ccccc}
8 & 7 & 6 & 5 & 6 \\
5 & 7 & 11 & 7 & 7 \\
7 & 8 & 7 & 9 & 6 \\
8 & 6 & 5 & 9 & 7
\end{array}
$$

(a) Construct a frequency table from the above data and add a cumulative frequency column. 2

(b) For this data, find:

 (i) the median; 1

 (ii) the lower quartile; 1

 (iii) the upper quartile. 1

(c) Construct a boxplot for this data. 2

[Turn over

Marks

3. The diagram below represents a sphere.

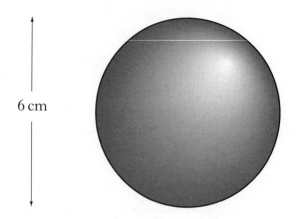

6 cm

The sphere has a diameter of 6 centimetres.

Calculate its volume.

Take π = 3·14.

2

4. (*a*) Factorise

$$x^2 + x - 6.$$

2

(*b*) Multiply out the brackets and collect like terms.

$$(3x + 2)(x^2 + 5x - 1)$$

3

Marks

5. The diagram shows a network of streets connecting certain landmarks in a town centre.

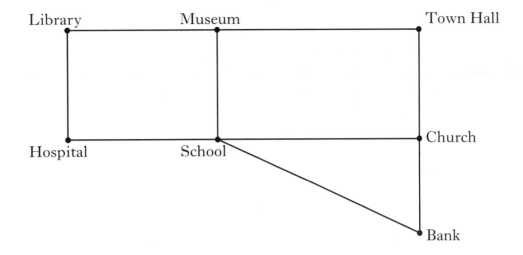

A bin lorry has to collect rubbish along every street shown.

Is it possible to do this without travelling any street more than once? Explain your answer.

2

6.

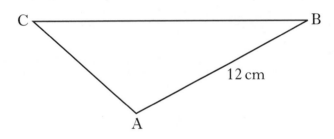

In triangle ABC, AB = 12 centimetres, sin C = $\frac{1}{2}$ and sin B = $\frac{1}{3}$.

Find the length of side AC.

3

[Turn over for Questions 7 and 8 on *Page six*

Marks

7. The size of each angle, $a°$, in a regular polygon is given by the formula

$$a = 180 - \frac{360}{n},$$

where n is the number of sides in the regular polygon.

(a) Calculate a when $n = 10$. **2**

(b) Calculate n when $a = 140$. **3**

8. The table below shows the monthly repayments to be made when money is borrowed from the Bank of Caledonia.

Repayments can be made with or without loan protection.

| | Monthly repayments: Bank of Caledonia | | | | | |
| | 24 months | | 36 months | | 48 months | |
Loan Amount	With Loan Protection	Without Loan Protection	With Loan Protection	Without Loan Protection	With Loan Protection	Without Loan Protection
£10 000	£495	£445	£343	£305	£277	£237
£8000	£395	£356	£275	£244	£222	£190
£5000	£247	£223	£172	£153	£139	£119
£4000	£198	£179	£138	£123	£111	£95

Jeremy borrows £8000 over 36 months **without** loan protection.

After 28 months, he is made redundant and is unable to pay the remainder of the loan.

His brother, Peter, agrees to make the remaining payments.

How much does Peter pay in total? **3**

[END OF QUESTION PAPER]

X101/204

| NATIONAL QUALIFICATIONS 2010 | FRIDAY, 21 MAY 2.05 PM – 3.35 AM | MATHEMATICS INTERMEDIATE 2 Units 1, 2 and Applications of Mathematics Paper 2 |

Read carefully

1 **Calculators may be used in this paper.**

2 Full credit will be given only where the solution contains appropriate working.

3 Square-ruled paper is provided.

FORMULAE LIST

Sine rule: $\dfrac{a}{\sin A} = \dfrac{b}{\sin B} = \dfrac{c}{\sin C}$

Cosine rule: $a^2 = b^2 + c^2 - 2bc\cos A$ or $\cos A = \dfrac{b^2 + c^2 - a^2}{2bc}$

Area of a triangle: Area $= \frac{1}{2}ab\sin C$

Volume of a sphere: Volume $= \frac{4}{3}\pi r^3$

Volume of a cone: Volume $= \frac{1}{3}\pi r^2 h$

Volume of a cylinder: Volume $= \pi r^2 h$

Standard deviation: $s = \sqrt{\dfrac{\sum(x - \bar{x})^2}{n-1}} = \sqrt{\dfrac{\sum x^2 - (\sum x)^2/n}{n-1}}$, where n is the sample size.

Page two

Marks

ALL questions should be attempted.

1. An industrial machine costs £176 500.

    Its value depreciates by 4·25% each year.

    How much is it worth after 3 years?

    Give your answer correct to **three** significant figures.   **4**

2. Paul conducts a survey to find the most popular school lunch.

    - 30 pupils vote for Pasta
    - 40 pupils vote for Baked Potato
    - 2 pupils vote for Salad

    Paul wishes to draw a pie chart to illustrate his data. How many degrees must he use for each sector in his pie chart?

    Do not draw the pie chart.   **2**

3. The scattergraph shows the taxi fare, p pounds, plotted against the distance travelled, m miles. A line of best fit has been drawn.

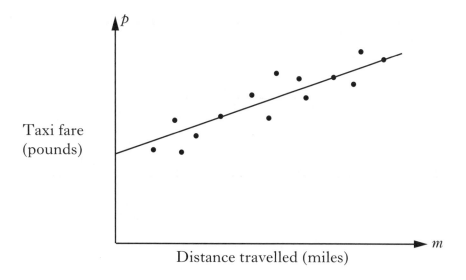

    The equation of the line of best fit is $p = 2 + 1·5\,m$.

    Use this equation to predict the taxi fare for a journey of 6 miles.   **1**

[Turn over

Marks

4. A rugby team scored the following points in a series of matches.

    13   7   0   9   7   8   5

    (a) For this sample, calculate:

    (i)   the mean;   1

    (ii) the standard deviation.   3

    Show clearly all your working.

    The following season, the team appoints a new coach.

    A similar series of matches produces a mean of 27 and a standard deviation of 3·25.

    (b) Make two valid comparisons about the performance of the team under the new coach.   2

5. Solve algebraically the system of equations

    $$2x - 5y = 24$$
    $$7x + 8y = 33.$$ 3

6. The network diagram below shows the time it takes **three** friends to tidy a flat. All times are in minutes.

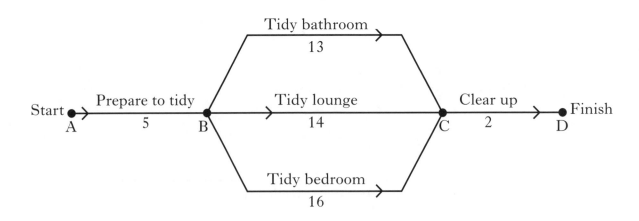

Guests are due to arrive in 20 minutes.

Will the flat be tidy on time?

Give a reason for your answer.   1

Marks

7. Sam sells used cars. She keeps a record of her profits on a spreadsheet.

	A	B	C	D	E
1	Make of Car	Cost Price	Selling Price	Profit	Profit (%)
2					
3	Sultan	£2500	£3800	£1300	52
4	Astral 4	£3600	£4800		
5	Ventra	£2000	£3000		
6	Satellite 5	£7250	£8120		
7	Phoenix	£2800	£3080		

(*a*)   What formula would be used to enter the profit in cell D6?   1

(*b*)   The result of the formula =D6/B6*100 is to appear in cell E6.

What value will appear in cell E6?   3

8. The cost of electricity per quarter to a sample of homes in Bellrock Avenue was recorded.

The results are shown in the histogram below.

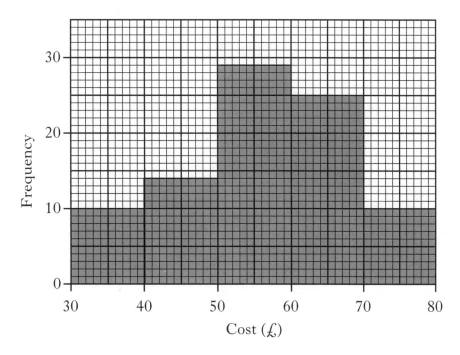

Estimate the value of the mode.   1

[Turn over

Marks

9. The ends of a magazine rack are identical.

   Each end is a sector of a circle with radius 14 centimetres.
   The angle in each sector is 65°.

   The sectors are joined by two rectangles, each with length 40 centimetres.

   The exterior is covered by material. What area of material is required?

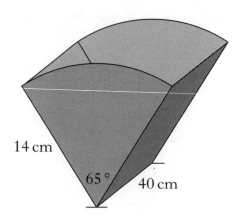

14 cm

65° 40 cm

4

10. The diagram below represents a rectangular garden with length $(x + 7)$ metres and breadth $(x + 3)$ metres.

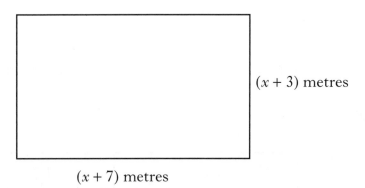

$(x + 3)$ metres

$(x + 7)$ metres

Show that the area, A square metres, of the garden is given by

$$A = x^2 + 10x + 21.$$

2

Marks

11. A cylindrical container has a volume of 3260 cubic centimetres.

    The radius of the cross section is 6·4 centimetres.

    Calculate the height of the cylinder.

3

12. Two ships have located a wreck on the sea bed.

    In the diagram below, the points P and Q represent the two ships and the point R represents the wreck.

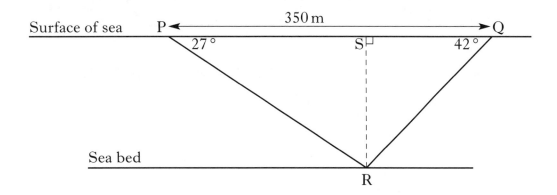

    The angle of depression of R from P is 27°.
    The angle of depression of R from Q is 42°.
    The distance PQ is 350 metres.

    Calculate QS, the distance ship Q has to travel to be directly above the wreck.

    Do not use a scale drawing.

5

[Turn over

Marks

13. Ocean World has an underwater viewing tunnel.

The diagram below shows the cross-section of the tunnel. It consists of part of a circle with a horizontal base.

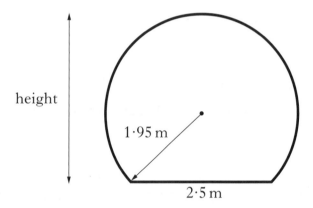

The radius of the circle is 1·95 metres and the width of the base is 2·5 metres.

Calculate the height of the tunnel.

4

Marks

14. Shaheen works in a call centre. Her basic rate of pay is £6·40 per hour.

She is paid time and a half for working overtime in the evening and double time for working overtime at the weekend.

One week she works 35 hours at the basic rate and 6 hours overtime in the evening. She also works overtime at the weekend.

Shaheen's gross pay for the week is £320.

How many hours does she work at the weekend?   **4**

15. The marks of a group of students in their Intermediate 2 Mathematics examination were recorded.

The cumulative frequency results are shown below.

Marks (m)	*Cumulative Frequency*
$0 \leq m < 10$	1
$10 \leq m < 20$	5
$20 \leq m < 30$	12
$30 \leq m < 40$	30
$40 \leq m < 50$	48
$50 \leq m < 60$	55
$60 \leq m < 70$	59
$70 \leq m < 80$	60

(*a*) Using squared paper, draw a cumulative frequency diagram for this data.   **3**

(*b*) From your diagram, estimate:

(i) the lower quartile;   **1**

(ii) the upper quartile.   **1**

(*c*) Calculate the semi-interquartile range.   **1**

[END OF QUESTION PAPER]

[BLANK PAGE]

INTERMEDIATE 2

2011

[BLANK PAGE]

X101/202

| NATIONAL QUALIFICATIONS 2011 | WEDNESDAY, 18 MAY 1.00 PM – 1.45 PM | MATHEMATICS INTERMEDIATE 2 Units 1, 2 and Applications of Mathematics Paper 1 (Non-calculator) |

Read carefully

1 **You may NOT use a calculator.**

2 Full credit will be given only where the solution contains appropriate working.

3 Square-ruled paper is provided. If you make use of this, you should write your name on it clearly and put it inside your answer booklet.

FORMULAE LIST

Sine rule: $\dfrac{a}{\sin A} = \dfrac{b}{\sin B} = \dfrac{c}{\sin C}$

Cosine rule: $a^2 = b^2 + c^2 - 2bc \cos A$ or $\cos A = \dfrac{b^2 + c^2 - a^2}{2bc}$

Area of a triangle: $\text{Area} = \tfrac{1}{2} ab \sin C$

Volume of a sphere: $\text{Volume} = \tfrac{4}{3} \pi r^3$

Volume of a cone: $\text{Volume} = \tfrac{1}{3} \pi r^2 h$

Volume of a cylinder: $\text{Volume} = \pi r^2 h$

Standard deviation: $s = \sqrt{\dfrac{\sum (x - \bar{x})^2}{n-1}} = \sqrt{\dfrac{\sum x^2 - (\sum x)^2 / n}{n-1}}$, where n is the sample size.

Marks

ALL questions should be attempted.

1. Sandi takes the bus to work each day.

   Over a two week period, she records the number of minutes the bus is late each day. The results are shown below.

   $$5 \quad 6 \quad 15 \quad 0 \quad 6 \quad 11 \quad 2 \quad 9 \quad 8 \quad 7$$

   (a) From the above data, find:

      (i) the median;   1

     (ii) the lower quartile;   1

   (iii) the upper quartile.   1

   (b) Construct a boxplot for the data.   2

   Sandi decides to take the train over the next two week period and records the number of minutes the train is late each day.

   The boxplot, drawn below, was constructed for the new data.

   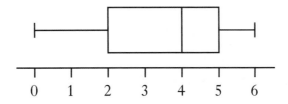

   (c) Compare the two boxplots and comment.   1

2. Factorise

   $$x^2 - 4x - 21.$$ 2

3. Multiply out the brackets and collect like terms.

   $$5x + (3x + 2)(2x - 7)$$ 3

[Turn over

Marks

4. A circle, centre O, is shown below.

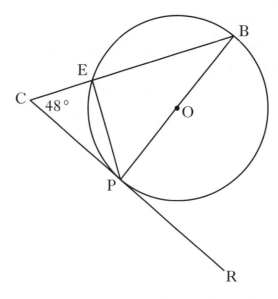

In the circle

- PB is a diameter
- CR is a tangent to the circle at point P
- Angle BCP is 48°.

Calculate the size of angle EPR.   3

5. The approximate stopping distance of a car can be found by using the formula

$$D = \frac{1}{3}\left(S + \frac{S^2}{20}\right)$$

where D metres is the approximate stopping distance
and S miles per hour is the speed before braking.

Calculate the approximate stopping distance when the speed before braking is
30 miles per hour.   3

Marks

6.   Below is the summary part of Geetha's Credit Card statement at the end of May.

Briggs Bank

CREDIT CARD STATEMENT

Summary as at 21 May 2011

Credit Limit	£4000
Available Credit	£3760

Balance from previous statement	£0·00
New Transactions	£240·00
Interest	£0·00
Balance owed	£240·00
Minimum payment due	£7·20
Payment due date	15 June 2011

Interest will be charged at 1% per month on any outstanding balance.

Geetha pays the minimum payment.

She does not use the credit card again.

What is the "Balance owed" in her next statement?   2

[Turn over

Marks

7.

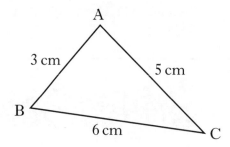

In triangle ABC, show that $\cos B = \dfrac{5}{9}$.   **3**

8. A straight line is represented by the equation $y = mx + c$.

Sketch a possible straight line graph to illustrate this equation when $m > 0$ and $c < 0$.   **2**

Marks

9. A catering company supplies the airports at Aberdeen (A), Edinburgh (E), Glasgow (G), Newcastle (N) and Prestwick (P). The network diagram below represents the distances in miles by road between the airports.

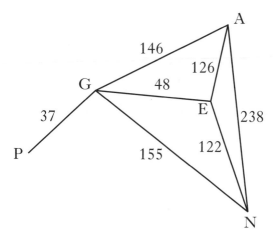

Catering supplies are distributed by van from Prestwick to the other airports. The van does not need to return to Prestwick.

(a) Copy and complete the tree diagram to show **all** the possible routes the van can take.

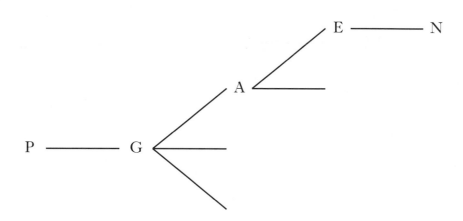

3

(b) The van driver decides he wants to finish the journey at **Newcastle**.

What is the shortest distance he has to drive to finish the journey at Newcastle?

Explain your answer.

2

[Turn over for Question 10 on *Page eight*

Marks

10.

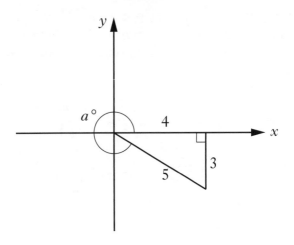

Write down the value of $\cos a^{\circ}$.   **1**

[END OF QUESTION PAPER]

X101/204

NATIONAL QUALIFICATIONS 2011	WEDNESDAY, 18 MAY 2.05 PM – 3.35 PM	MATHEMATICS INTERMEDIATE 2 Units 1, 2 and Applications of Mathematics Paper 2

Read carefully

1 **Calculators may be used in this paper.**

2 Full credit will be given only where the solution contains appropriate working.

3 Square-ruled paper is provided. If you make use of this, you should write your name on it clearly and put it inside your answer booklet.

FORMULAE LIST

Sine rule: $\dfrac{a}{\sin A} = \dfrac{b}{\sin B} = \dfrac{c}{\sin C}$

Cosine rule: $a^2 = b^2 + c^2 - 2bc \cos A$ or $\cos A = \dfrac{b^2 + c^2 - a^2}{2bc}$

Area of a triangle: $\text{Area} = \frac{1}{2}ab \sin C$

Volume of a sphere: $\text{Volume} = \frac{4}{3}\pi r^3$

Volume of a cone: $\text{Volume} = \frac{1}{3}\pi r^2 h$

Volume of a cylinder: $\text{Volume} = \pi r^2 h$

Standard deviation: $s = \sqrt{\dfrac{\sum (x - \bar{x})^2}{n-1}} = \sqrt{\dfrac{\sum x^2 - (\sum x)^2 / n}{n-1}}$, where n is the sample size.

Marks

ALL questions should be attempted.

1.

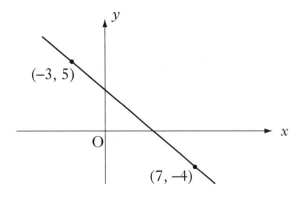

Calculate the gradient of the straight line passing through the points (–3, 5) and (7, –4).   1

2. It is estimated that house prices will increase at the rate of 3·15% per annum.

A house is valued at £134 750. If its value increases at the predicted rate, calculate its value after 3 years.

Give your answer correct to **four** significant figures.   4

3. The Battle of Largs in 1263 is commemorated by a monument known as The Pencil.

This monument is in the shape of a cylinder with a cone on top.

The cylinder part has diameter 3 metres and height 15 metres.

(a) Calculate the volume of the **cylinder** part of The Pencil.   2

The volume of the **cone** part of The Pencil is 5·7 cubic metres.

(b) Calculate the **total** height of The Pencil.   3

[Turn over

Marks

4. The diagram below shows a sector of a circle, centre C.

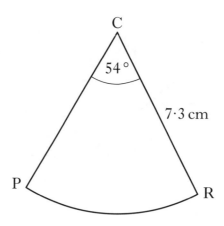

The radius of the circle is 7·3 centimetres and angle PCR is 54°.

Calculate the area of the sector PCR.   **3**

5. A sample of six boxes contains the following numbers of pins per box.

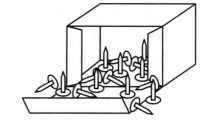

43   39   41   40   39   44

(a) For the above data, calculate:

  (i) the mean;   **1**

  (ii) the standard deviation.   **3**

The company which produces the pins claims that "the mean number of pins per box is 40 ± 2 and the standard deviation is less than 3".

(b) Does the data in part (a) support the claim made by the company?

  Give reasons for your answer.   **2**

Marks

6. Alan is taking part in a quiz. He is awarded x points for each correct answer and y points for each wrong answer. During the quiz, Alan gets 24 questions correct and 6 wrong. He scores 60 points.

   (a) Write down an equation in x and y which satisfies the above condition. **1**

   Helen also takes part in the quiz. She gets 20 questions correct and 10 wrong. She scores 40 points.

   (b) Write down a second equation in x and y which satisfies this condition. **1**

   (c) Calculate the score for David who gets 17 correct and 13 wrong. **4**

7. The table below gives the **monthly** repayments from three different banks on a £10 000 loan repaid over **five years**.

| Name of Bank | Monthly Repayments | |
	With payment protection	Without payment protection
Savewell	£245·39	£214·39
Finesave	£260·58	£205·65
Wisespend	£263·17	£214·70

Emily borrowed £10 000 and paid it back over five years. The cost of the loan was £2339. Which bank was the loan from and did she take it with or without payment protection? **3**

[Turn over

Marks

8. In a race, organisers record how long each runner takes to complete the course. The results are shown in the cumulative frequency curve below.

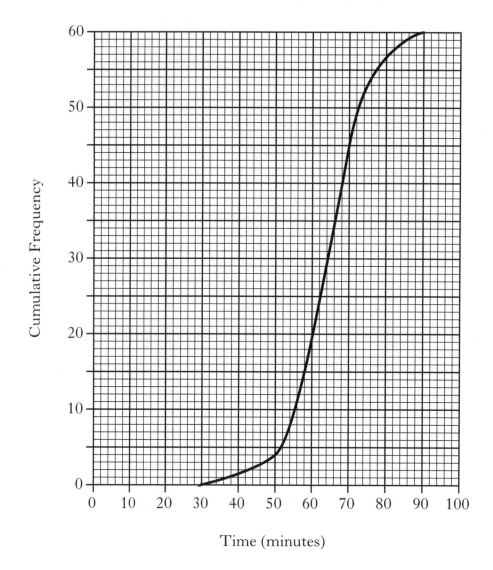

Time (minutes)

(*a*) How many runners completed the course in 50 minutes or less?   **1**

(*b*) Calculate the semi-interquartile range for the data represented in the diagram.   **3**

Marks

9. Jack works a basic week of 35 hours.

   Any overtime is paid at time and a half.

   One week he works for 39 hours and is paid £255·84.

   How much is he paid for each hour of **overtime** that he works?

3

[Turn over

Marks

10. Seamus has been offered jobs by both Paywell and Highpay. He constructs a spreadsheet to allow him to compare the salaries he has been offered. Part of the spreadsheet is shown below.

	A	B	C	D	E
1			**Paywell**		
2		**Basic salary**	**Bonus**	**Annual gross salary**	**Total earned to date**
3					
4	**Year 1**	£15,000	£1,250	£16,250	£16,250
5	**Year 2**	£15,600	£1,300	£16,900	£33,150
6	**Year 3**	£16,200	£1,350	£17,550	
7	**Year 4**	£16,800	£1,400		
8	**Year 5**	£17,400			
9					
10			**Highpay**		
11		**Basic salary**	**Bonus**	**Annual gross salary**	**Total earned to date**
12					
13	**Year 1**	£12,000	£1,200	£13,200	£13,200
14	**Year 2**	£14,000	£1,400	£15,400	£28,600
15	**Year 3**	£16,000	£1,600	£17,600	
16	**Year 4**	£18,000	£1,800		
17	**Year 5**	£20,000	£2,000		

Paywell offers an initial basic salary of £15 000, with a rise of £600 per annum and a bonus of one month's salary.

Highpay offers an initial basic salary of £12 000, with a rise of £2000 per annum and a bonus of 10% of his annual salary.

(a) Write down the **formula** to enter in cell C4 the bonus for Year 1.   1

(b) Write down the **formula** to enter in cell E8 the total salary earned after 5 years with Paywell.   1

(c) What will appear in cell E8?   2

(d) Seamus intends to stay with the company for only 3 years.

Which company will allow him to earn more money in that time?   2

Marks

11.

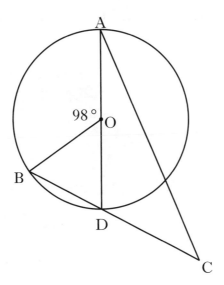

AD is a diameter of a circle, centre O.

B is a point on the circumference of the circle.

The chord BD is extended to a point C, outside the circle.

Angle BOA = 98°.

DC = 9 centimetres. The radius of the circle is 7 centimetres.

Calculate the length of AC.

5

[Turn over for Question 12 on *Page ten*

Marks

12. A circular saw can be adjusted to change the depth of blade that is exposed below the horizontal guide.

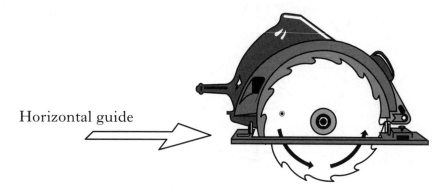

Horizontal guide

The circle, centre O, below represents the blade and the line AB represents part of the horizontal guide.

This blade has a radius of 110 millimetres.

If AB has length 140 millimetres, calculate the depth, d millimetres, of saw exposed.

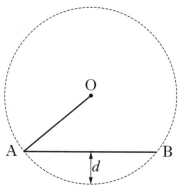

4

[END OF QUESTION PAPER]

INTERMEDIATE 2

2012

HODDER
GIBSON
LEARN MORE

[BLANK PAGE]

X101/11/01

| NATIONAL QUALIFICATIONS 2012 | MONDAY, 21 MAY 9.00 AM – 9.45 AM | MATHEMATICS INTERMEDIATE 2 Units 1, 2 and Applications of Mathematics Paper 1 (Non-calculator) |

Read carefully

1   **You may <u>NOT</u> use a calculator.**

2   Full credit will be given only where the solution contains appropriate working.

3   Square-ruled paper is provided. If you make use of this, you should write your name on it clearly and put it inside your answer booklet.

FORMULAE LIST

Sine rule: $\dfrac{a}{\sin A} = \dfrac{b}{\sin B} = \dfrac{c}{\sin C}$

Cosine rule: $a^2 = b^2 + c^2 - 2bc \cos A$ or $\cos A = \dfrac{b^2 + c^2 - a^2}{2bc}$

Area of a triangle: $\text{Area} = \frac{1}{2} ab \sin C$

Volume of a sphere: $\text{Volume} = \frac{4}{3} \pi r^3$

Volume of a cone: $\text{Volume} = \frac{1}{3} \pi r^2 h$

Volume of a cylinder: $\text{Volume} = \pi r^2 h$

Standard deviation: $s = \sqrt{\dfrac{\sum (x - \bar{x})^2}{n-1}} = \sqrt{\dfrac{\sum x^2 - (\sum x)^2 / n}{n-1}}$, where n is the sample size.

ALL questions should be attempted.   *Marks*

1. The National Debt of the United Kingdom was recently calculated as

   £1 157 818 887 139.

   Round this amount to four significant figures.   **1**

2. A teacher recorded the marks, out of ten, of a group of pupils for a spelling test.

Mark	Frequency
5	2
6	5
7	6
8	11
9	9
10	2

   (*a*) Copy the frequency table and add a cumulative frequency column.   **1**

   (*b*) For this data, find:

     (i) the median;   **1**

     (ii) the lower quartile;   **1**

     (iii) the upper quartile.   **1**

   (*c*) Draw a boxplot to illustrate this data.   **2**

                                                             [Turn over

Marks

3. The straight line with equation $4x + 3y = 36$ cuts the y-axis at A.

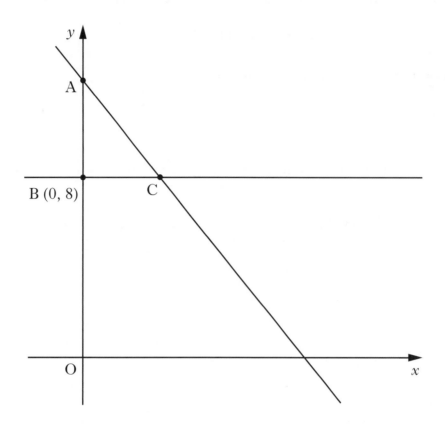

(a) Find the coordinates of A.   1

This line meets the line through B (0, 8), parallel to the x-axis, at C as shown above.

(b) Find the coordinates of C.   2

Marks

4.

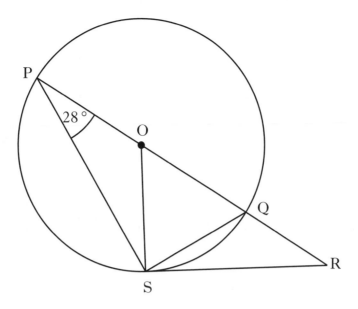

In the above diagram,

- O is the centre of the circle
- PQ is a diameter of the circle
- PQR is a straight line
- RS is a tangent to the circle at S
- angle OPS is 28°.

Calculate the size of angle QRS.   **3**

5. One weekend, the attendances at five Premier League football matches were recorded.

| 8 900 | 12 700 | 59 200 | 10 300 | 9 700 |

The median attendance is 10 300.

(*a*) Calculate the mean attendance.   **1**

(*b*) Which of the two "averages" – the mean or the median – is more representative of the data?

You must explain your answer.   **1**

[Turn over

Marks

6. During an athletics meeting, the distances of 80 attempts in the discus competition are recorded.

The cumulative frequency curve derived from the distances is shown below.

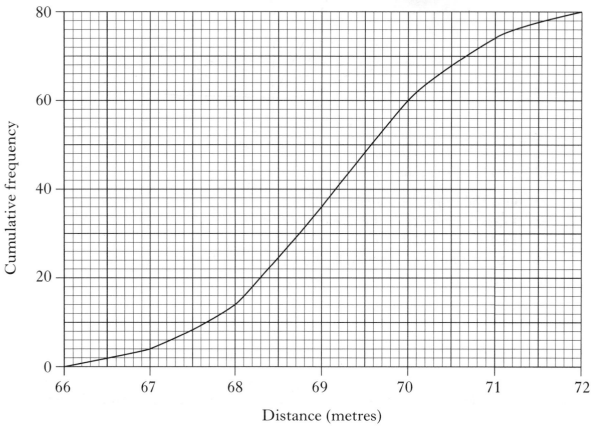

Distance (metres)

Use the curve to find the interquartile range of the distances.   **3**

Marks

7.

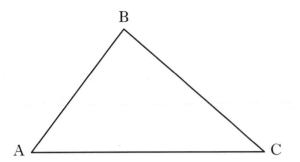

The area of triangle ABC is 20 square centimetres.

AC = 16 centimetres and $\sin C = \frac{1}{4}$.

Calculate the length of BC.   **2**

8. (*a*) Factorise

$$a^2 + 2ab + b^2.$$ **1**

(*b*) Hence, or otherwise, find the value of

$$94^2 + 2 \times 94 \times 6 + 6^2.$$ **2**

[Turn over

Marks

9. Maureen has her electricity supplied by the Use Less Power Company. She has designed a spreadsheet to check her bills.

	A	B	C	D	E	F	G	H	I
1	Use Less Power Company					Cost per unit = 16p			
2									
3									
4		Previous Reading	Present Reading	Units Used	Cost of Units	Standing Charge	Sub-total	VAT at 5%	Total cost
5									
6	Jan–Mar	75 812	76 915	1103	£176·48	£14·99	£191·47	£9·57	£201·04
7	Apr–Jun	76 915	77 408	493	£78·88	£14·99	£93·87	£4·69	£98·56
8	Jul–Sep	77 408	77 632	224	£35·84	£14·99	£50·83		
9	Oct–Dec	77 632	78 519	887					

She receives a bill each quarter. Electricity costs 16p per unit and there is a standing charge of £14·99 per quarter.

(a) Write down the **formula** to enter in cell E8 the cost of the units for the period from July to September.   1

(b) Write down the **formula** to enter in cell H8 the cost of the VAT at 5% for the period from July to September.   1

(c) What value will appear in cell I8?   2

Marks

10. A copy of Logan Pollock's payslip is shown below for one week in February.

Name L. Pollock	Employee No. 027	Tax Code 64L	Week Ending 14/02/2012
Basic Pay £296·00	**Overtime Pay** £55·50	**Bonus** —	**Gross Pay** £351·50
National Insurance £20·04	**Income Tax** £45·40	**Pension** £21·09	**Deductions** £86·53
			Net Pay £264 ·97

Logan worked 40 hours for his basic pay.

If overtime was paid at the rate of "time and a half", calculate how many hours of overtime he worked during that week.

3

[END OF QUESTION PAPER]

[BLANK PAGE]

X101/11/02

NATIONAL QUALIFICATIONS 2012	MONDAY, 21 MAY 10.05 AM – 11.35 AM	**MATHEMATICS** INTERMEDIATE 2 Units 1, 2 and Applications of Mathematics Paper 2

Read carefully

1   **Calculators may be used in this paper.**

2   Full credit will be given only where the solution contains appropriate working.

3   Square-ruled paper is provided. If you make use of this, you should write your name on it clearly and put it inside your answer booklet.

FORMULAE LIST

Sine rule: $\dfrac{a}{\sin A} = \dfrac{b}{\sin B} = \dfrac{c}{\sin C}$

Cosine rule: $a^2 = b^2 + c^2 - 2bc\cos A \ \text{ or } \ \cos A = \dfrac{b^2 + c^2 - a^2}{2bc}$

Area of a triangle: $\text{Area} = \frac{1}{2}ab\sin C$

Volume of a sphere: $\text{Volume} = \frac{4}{3}\pi r^3$

Volume of a cone: $\text{Volume} = \frac{1}{3}\pi r^2 h$

Volume of a cylinder: $\text{Volume} = \pi r^2 h$

Standard deviation: $s = \sqrt{\dfrac{\sum (x - \bar{x})^2}{n-1}} = \sqrt{\dfrac{\sum x^2 - (\sum x)^2 / n}{n-1}}$, where n is the sample size.

ALL questions should be attempted.   *Marks*

1. The diagram below shows a circle, centre C.

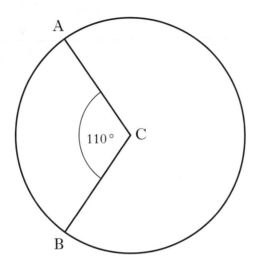

The circumference of the circle is 40·8 centimetres.

Calculate the length of the minor arc AB.   2

2. Multiply out the brackets and collect like terms.

$(3x - 5)(x^2 + 2x - 6)$ 3

[Turn over

Marks

3. A health food shop produces cod liver oil capsules for its customers.

Each capsule is in the shape of a cylinder with hemispherical ends as shown in the diagram below.

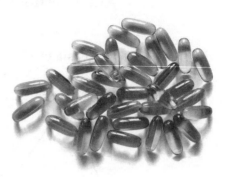

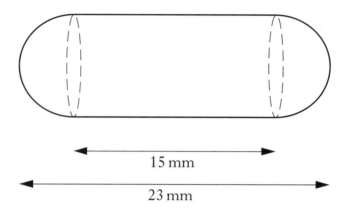

15 mm

23 mm

The total length of the capsule is 23 millimetres and the length of the cylinder is 15 millimetres.

Calculate the volume of one cod liver oil capsule.

4

Marks

4. Stationery Systems offers a photocopying service to its customers. The flowchart below shows how charges are calculated for any number of copies.

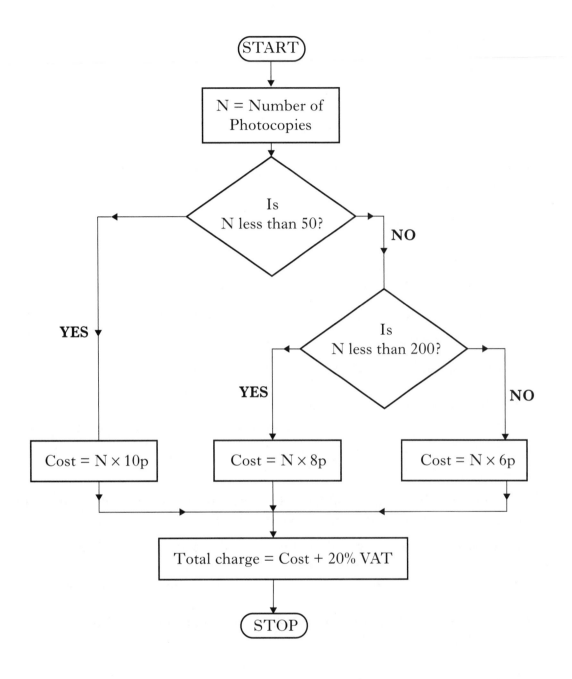

Use the flowchart to calculate the total charge for Kamran who makes 360 photocopies.   4

[Turn over

Marks

5. A ten-pin bowling team recorded the following six scores in a match.

    134　　102　　127　　98　　104　　131

   (a) For this sample calculate:

      (i) the mean;

      (ii) the standard deviation.

      Show clearly all your working.　　　　4

   In their second match their six scores have a mean of 116 and a standard deviation of 12·2.

   (b) Consider the 5 statements written below.

      1　The total of the scores is the same in both matches.
      2　The total of the scores is greater in the first match.
      3　The total of the scores is greater in the second match.
      4　In the first match the scores are more spread out.
      5　In the second match the scores are more spread out.

      Which of these statements is/are true?　　　　2

6. Three groups are booking a holiday. The first group consists of 6 adults and 2 children. The total cost of their holiday is £3148.

   Let x pounds be the cost for an adult and y pounds be the cost for a child.

   (a) Write down an equation in x and y which satisfies the above information.　　　　1

   The second group books the same holiday for 5 adults and 3 children. The total cost of their holiday is £3022.

   (b) Write down a second equation in x and y which satisfies this information.　　　　1

   (c) The third group books the same holiday for 2 adults and 4 children. The travel agent calculates that the total cost is £2056.

      Has this group been overcharged?

      Justify your answer.　　　　4

Marks

7. A network diagram is shown below.

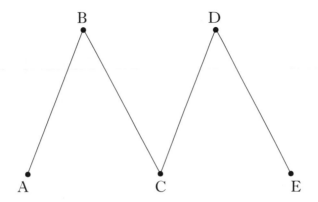

Copy the diagram and add one arc so that all the nodes are even. 1

8. The Bank of Salamander offers loans to its customers.

The table shown below can be used to calculate loan repayments.

		60 months	48 months	24 months
		Monthly repayment (£)	Monthly repayment (£)	Monthly repayment (£)
With payment protection	£20 000	467·85	555·43	998·23
	£15 000	351·89	417·57	749·67
	£7500	177·94	210·79	376·84
Without payment protection	£20 000	388·65	471·72	888·47
	£15 000	292·49	354·79	667·35
	£7500	148·29	179·40	335·68

Amy requires to borrow £15 000 to buy a car.

How much will the loan cost her if she repays it over 24 months, **without payment protection**? 3

[Turn over

Marks

9. The Room Index is used to calculate the amount of light needed in a workroom.

   The formula for the Room Index, R, is

   $$R = \frac{LW}{H(L+W)}$$

   where L metres is the length of the room,
   W metres is the width of the room
   and H metres is the height of the light above the work surface.

   Calculate the Room Index for a workroom 4·4 metres long and 3·2 metres wide with the light 1·4 metres above the work surface.

3

10. A tanker delivers oil to garages.

    The tank has a circular cross-section as shown in the diagram below.

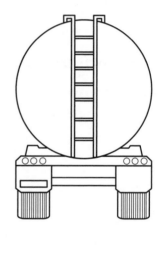

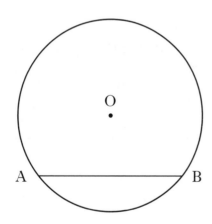

Depth of oil

The radius of the circle, centre O, is 1·9 metres.

The width of the surface of the oil, represented by AB in the diagram, is 2·2 metres.

Calculate the depth of the oil in the tanker.

4

Marks

11. A dental practice keeps a record of the number of patients visiting the surgery over a period of time.

The information is shown below.

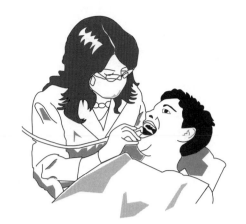

Number of patients	Number of days
6 – 10	4
11 – 15	8
16 – 20	10
21 – 25	18
26 – 30	7
31 – 35	3

Taking the number of patients to be at the mid-point of each interval, calculate the mean number of patients visiting the surgery per day.　　5

[Turn over

Marks

12. A yacht and a canoe can be seen from a clifftop.

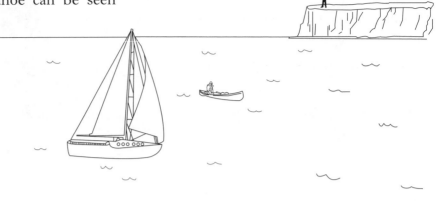

In the diagram below, Y and C represent the positions of the yacht and the canoe.

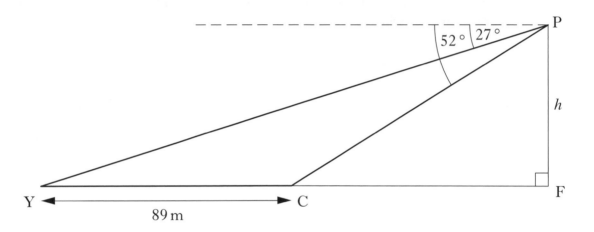

From a point P on the clifftop:

- the angle of depression of the yacht is 27°;
- the angle of depression of the canoe is 52°.

The distance between the yacht and the canoe is 89 metres.

Calculate the height, h, metres, of the cliff.

5

Marks

13. Due to the threat of global warming, scientists recommended in 2010 that the emissions of greenhouse gases should be reduced by 50% by the year 2050.

The government decided to reduce the emissions of greenhouse gases by 15% **every ten years**, starting in the year 2010.

Will the scientists' recommendations have been achieved by 2050?

You must give a reason for your answer.   4

[END OF QUESTION PAPER]

[BLANK PAGE]

[BLANK PAGE]

X101/11/01

NATIONAL QUALIFICATIONS 2013	WEDNESDAY, 22 MAY 9.00 AM – 9.45 AM	**MATHEMATICS** INTERMEDIATE 2 Units 1, 2 and Applications of Mathematics Paper 1 (Non-calculator)

Read carefully

1   **You may NOT use a calculator.**

2   Full credit will be given only where the solution contains appropriate working.

3   Square-ruled paper is provided. If you make use of this, you should write your name on it clearly and put it inside your answer booklet.

FORMULAE LIST

Sine rule: $\dfrac{a}{\sin A} = \dfrac{b}{\sin B} = \dfrac{c}{\sin C}$

Cosine rule: $a^2 = b^2 + c^2 - 2bc \cos A$ or $\cos A = \dfrac{b^2 + c^2 - a^2}{2bc}$

Area of a triangle: $\text{Area} = \frac{1}{2}ab \sin C$

Volume of a sphere: $\text{Volume} = \frac{4}{3}\pi r^3$

Volume of a cone: $\text{Volume} = \frac{1}{3}\pi r^2 h$

Volume of a cylinder: $\text{Volume} = \pi r^2 h$

Standard deviation: $s = \sqrt{\dfrac{\sum (x - \bar{x})^2}{n-1}} = \sqrt{\dfrac{\sum x^2 - (\sum x)^2 / n}{n-1}}$, where n is the sample size.

ALL questions should be attempted.

Marks

1. Factorise

$$6ab - 7bc.$$

1

2.

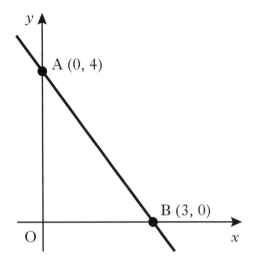

Find the equation of the straight line AB.

3

3. The diagram below shows a sector of a circle, centre C.

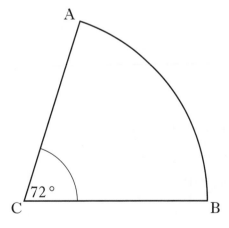

The radius of the circle is 5 centimetres and angle ACB is 72°.

Calculate the length of arc AB.

Take π = 3·14.

3

[Turn over

Marks

4. Solve algebraically the system of equations

$$2x - y = 10$$
$$4x + 5y = 6.$$

3

5.

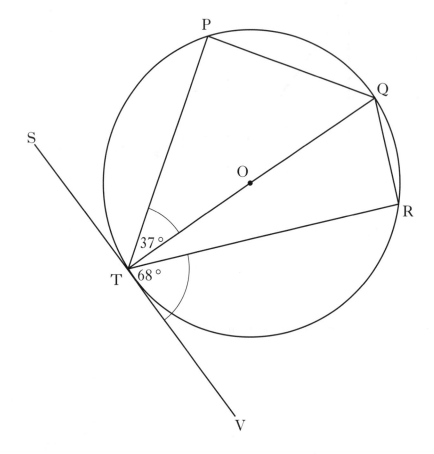

The tangent SV touches the circle, centre O, at T.

Angle PTQ is 37° and angle VTR is 68°.

Calculate the size of angle PQR.

3

Marks

6. The stem and leaf diagram shows the number of minutes on average spent on homework per night by a group of first year pupils.

```
1 | 0 5 5 5
2 | 0 1 2 2 3 5 5 8 9
3 | 0 5 5 6 6 7 8 9 9 9
4 | 2 4 4 5 6 7
5 | 0
```

n = 30   1 | 0 represents 10 minutes

(a) Using the above data find:

　(i) the median;   **1**

　(ii) the lower quartile;   **1**

　(iii) the upper quartile.   **1**

(b) Draw a boxplot to illustrate this data.   **2**

(c) A group of fourth year pupils was surveyed to find out how many minutes on average they spent on homework per night. The boxplot below was drawn for this data.

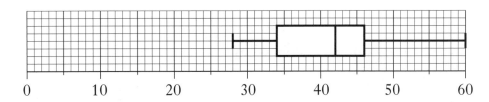

Compare the two boxplots and comment.   **2**

[Turn over

Marks

7. **Anna** tosses a coin **three** times.

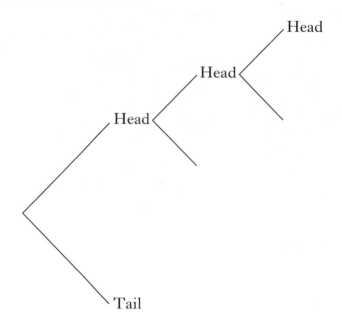

(a)   Copy and complete the above tree diagram to show **all** the possible results.   **3**

(b)   What is the probability that, out of three tosses, she gets exactly one tail?   **1**

8. The area of a trapezium is calculated by

$$A = \frac{1}{2}(a+b)h$$

where a and b are the parallel sides and h is the vertical distance between them.

Calculate the area of the trapezium below.

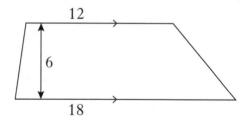

2

Marks

9. A company which manufactures light bulbs tests the lifetime of a sample of 100 bulbs. The results are shown in the cumulative frequency curve below.

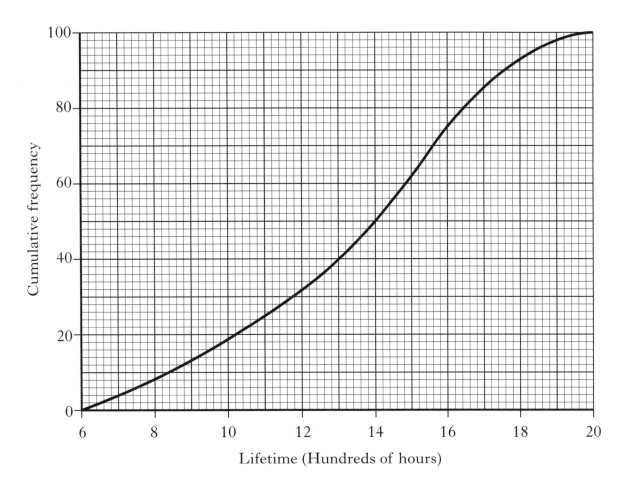

Lifetime (Hundreds of hours)

(a) State the median lifetime for the data represented in the diagram.   **1**

(b) Calculate the semi-interquartile range.   **3**

[END OF QUESTION PAPER]

[BLANK PAGE]

X101/11/02

NATIONAL
QUALIFICATIONS
2013

WEDNESDAY, 22 MAY
10.05 AM – 11.35 AM

MATHEMATICS
INTERMEDIATE 2
Units 1, 2 and
Applications of Mathematics
Paper 2

Read carefully

1   **Calculators may be used in this paper.**

2   Full credit will be given only where the solution contains appropriate working.

3   Square-ruled paper is provided. If you make use of this, you should write your name on it clearly and put it inside your answer booklet.

FORMULAE LIST

Sine rule: $\dfrac{a}{\sin A} = \dfrac{b}{\sin B} = \dfrac{c}{\sin C}$

Cosine rule: $a^2 = b^2 + c^2 - 2bc \cos A$ or $\cos A = \dfrac{b^2 + c^2 - a^2}{2bc}$

Area of a triangle: $\text{Area} = \frac{1}{2} ab \sin C$

Volume of a sphere: $\text{Volume} = \frac{4}{3} \pi r^3$

Volume of a cone: $\text{Volume} = \frac{1}{3} \pi r^2 h$

Volume of a cylinder: $\text{Volume} = \pi r^2 h$

Standard deviation: $s = \sqrt{\dfrac{\sum (x - \bar{x})^2}{n-1}} = \sqrt{\dfrac{\sum x^2 - (\sum x)^2 / n}{n-1}}$, where n is the sample size.

ALL questions should be attempted.   *Marks*

1. Multiply out the brackets and collect like terms.

   $$(x + 2)(x - 5) - 9x$$ 3

2. A company buys machinery worth £750 000.

   The value of the machinery depreciates by 20% per annum.

   The machinery will be replaced at the end of the year in which its value falls below half of its original value.

   After how many years should the machinery be replaced?

   You must explain your answer.   4

3. Erica works as a masseuse at a health club.

   Her March payslip, shown below, is only partly completed.

Name	Employee No.	Tax Code	Month
E. Roe	666	710L	March
Basic Pay	**Overtime Pay**	**Bonus**	**Gross Pay**
£1350	–		
Nat. Insurance	**Income Tax**	**Pension**	**Deductions**
£187·42	£297·59		
			Net Pay

   Erica is paid a bonus of £7·25 for each massage she does.

   During March she does 88 massages.

   Erica pays 6% of her Gross Pay into her Pension.

   Calculate Erica's Net Pay for March.   3

Marks

4. A sample of voters was asked how they intended to vote at the next election. The responses are shown below.

Party	Percentage
Scottish National Party (SNP)	35%
Labour (Lab)	30%
Liberal Democrat (Lib Dem)	15%
Conservative (Con)	10%
Others	10%

Construct a pie chart to illustrate this information.

Show all of your working.   3

5.

Monthly repayments for £10 000 loan		
	With Protection	Without Protection
Safeloan	£226·72	£191·26
Moneyback	£228·41	£196·41
Quickloan	£229·74	£200·71

The table above shows the monthly repayments charged by three companies for a loan of £10 000 repaid over 5 years.

Jennifer takes a £10 000 loan, over 5 years, with protection, from Moneyback.

Calculate the cost of her loan.   3

Marks

6. Part of Wendy's credit card statement is shown below.

Credit Limit = **£1000**	
Balance from previous statement	£25·78
Interest	£2·24
Cliff Petrol Station	£36·45
Save More Supermarket	£64·17
H R Brown	£13·25
Total Balance	£A
Minimum repayment	£B
Minimum repayment = 2·5% of balance or £5, whichever is greater	

Calculate the values of A and B. 3

7. Triangle PQR is shown below.

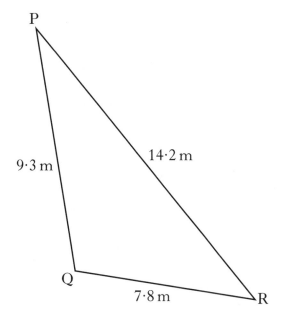

Calculate the size of angle QPR. 3

[Turn over

Marks

8. Harry often plays golf and the scores for some of his games are recorded below.

       84   78   87   80   81

    (*a*) For this sample calculate:

       (i) the mean;   **1**

       (ii) the standard deviation.   **3**

       Show clearly all your working.

    (*b*) His partner for these games is Tony, whose scores are listed below.

       104   98   107   100   101

       Write down the mean and standard deviation of Tony's scores.   **2**

9. A lead **cube**, of side 10 centimetres, is melted down.

    During this process 8% of the metal is lost.

    The remaining metal is then made into a **cone**, with radius 8 centimetres.

    Calculate the height of this cone.

    Give your answer correct to 2 significant figures.   **5**

Marks

10. A tree surgeon is asked to reduce the height of a tree.

    In the diagram below TB represents the original height of the tree and C is the point where the cut is to be made.

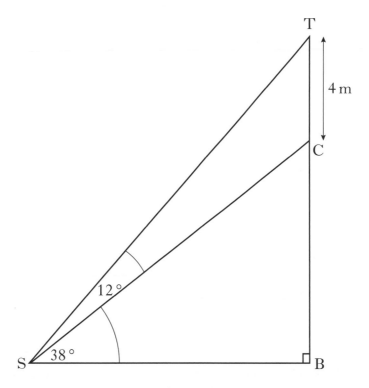

    The tree surgeon will reduce the height of the tree by 4 metres.

    Angle TSC = 12° and angle BSC = 38°.

    Calculate the height of the tree after it has been cut.

    Do not use a scale drawing.   5

[Turn over

Marks

11. The shape below is used as a logo in an advertising campaign. It is made up from segments of two identical circles.

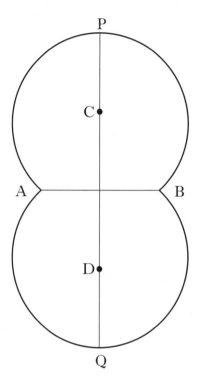

The points C and D are the centres of the circles and each circle has a radius of 24 centimetres.

AB is a common chord of length 30 centimetres.

Calculate the height of the logo, represented by the line PQ.   **5**

Marks

12. The flowchart below shows how to calculate a worker's gross weekly wage depending on the number of hours worked and the basic rate of pay per hour.

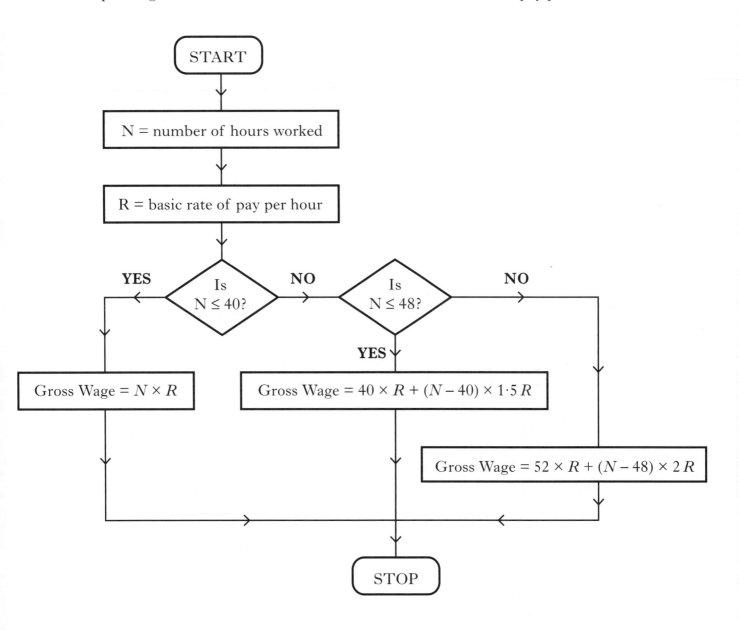

One week Frank worked 50 hours and had a Gross wage of £364.

Use the flowchart to calculate his basic rate of pay per hour.   **4**

[Turn over

Marks

13. Diagrams A and B show a histogram and a cumulative frequency curve respectively.

Diagram A   **Diagram B**

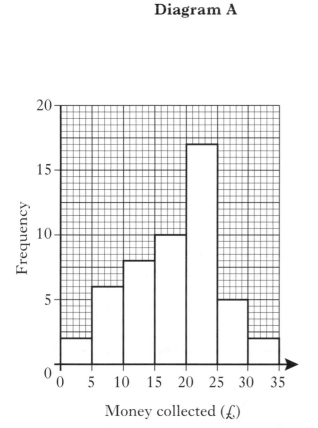 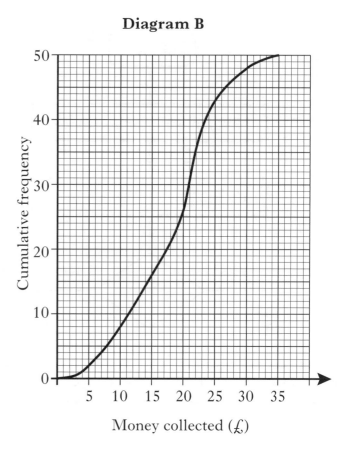

(a) Using the data in Diagram A, copy and complete the frequency table below.

Money collected (£)	Frequency
0·01 – 5·00	
5·01 – 10·00	
10·01 – 15·00	
15·01 – 20·00	
20·01 – 25·00	
25·01 – 30·00	
30·01 – 35·00	

1

Marks

13. (contined)

(*b*) Jim thinks that both Diagram A and Diagram B may have been drawn using the same set of data.

Is he correct?

Explain your answer, showing all your evidence.

2

[END OF QUESTION PAPER]

[BLANK PAGE]

INTERMEDIATE 2 | ANSWER SECTION

SQA INTERMEDIATE 2
MATHEMATICS: UNITS 1, 2 and APPLICATIONS
2009–2013

**MATHEMATICS INTERMEDIATE 2
UNITS 1, 2 AND APPLICATIONS
PAPER 1
2009 (NON-CALCULATOR)**

1. (a)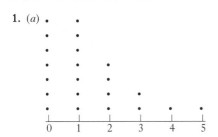

   (b) A

2. $y = 3x - 1$

3. $(x - 8)(x + 3)$

4. $2x^3 + 7x^2 - 16x - 5$

5. (a) (i) 58·5 (ii) 11

   (b) In December, the marks (on average) are better and less spread out

6. Any value for a such that $270 < a < 360$.

7. -1

8.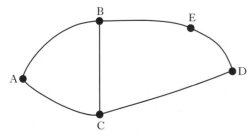

9. (a) =SUM(E6:E9)

   (b) =D6*(1+B2/100)

10. (a) S = 700cm^2

    (b) a = 9cm

**MATHEMATICS INTERMEDIATE 2
UNITS 1, 2 AND APPLICATIONS
PAPER 2
2009**

1. There were 3 sales fewer in 2008 or There were fewer sales in 2008 because 2997 < 3000

2. (a) 172 cm
   (b) 4·8 cm

3. 882 000 mm^3

4. (a) $14x + 60y = 344·30$
   (b) $21x + 40y = 368·95$
   (c) A car costs £11·95 and a passenger £2·95

5. 313 square inches

6. 68·6°

7. £4851·36

8. £100

9. £642·50

10. 8·6 metres

11. 3·14 metres

12. 105 pence (or £1·05)

MATHEMATICS INTERMEDIATE 2
UNITS 1, 2 AND APPLICATIONS
PAPER 1
2010 (NON-CALCULATOR)

1. $y = -\frac{4}{3}x + 8$

2. (a)

Shoe size	frequency	cumulative frequency
5	3	3
6	4	7
7	7	14
8	3	17
9	2	19
10	0	19
11	1	20

   (b) (i) 7   (ii) 6   (iii) 8

   (c)

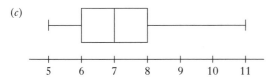

3. 113·04 cubic centimetres

4. (a) $(x + 3)(x - 2)$

   (b) $3x^3 + 17x^2 + 7x - 2$

5. Yes, with valid explanation e.g. Yes, because the route has only 2 odd vertices – museum and church.

6. 8 centimetres

7. (a) $a = 144$

   (b) $n = 9$

8. £1952

MATHEMATICS INTERMEDIATE 2
UNITS 1, 2 AND APPLICATIONS
PAPER 2
2010

1. £155 000

2. 150°, 200°, 10°

3. £11

4. (a) (i) 7   (ii) 3·958

   (b) The team scores more points under the new coach. The team is more consistent.

5. $x = 7, y = -2$

6. No, because it will take 23 minutes to tidy.

7. (a) = C6 − B6

   (b) 12

8. £58 (± 0·30)

9. 1342·35 square centimetres

10. Proof
    $(x + 7)(x + 3)$
    evidence of four correct terms
    $x^2 + 7x + 3x + 21$ leading to
    $x^2 + 10x + 21$

11. 25·3 centimetres

12. 126·5 metres

13. 3·45 metres

14. 3 hours

15. (a) cumulative frequency curve

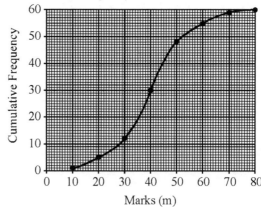

   (b) (i) 32   (ii) 48

   (c) 8

MATHEMATICS INTERMEDIATE 2 UNITS 1, 2 AND APPLICATIONS PAPER 1 2011 (NON-CALCULATOR)

1. (*a*) (i) $Q_2 = 6 \cdot 5$
    (ii) $Q_1 = 5$
    (iii) $Q_3 = 9$

(*b*)

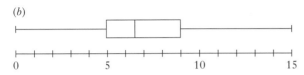

(*c*) The trains are not as late as the buses
or the trains are more reliable

2. $(x - 7)(x + 3)$

3. $6x^2 - 12x - 14$

4. $138°$

5. 25 metres

6. £235·13 **or** £235·12

7. To prove $\cos B = \dfrac{5}{9}$

$$\cos B = \frac{a^2 + c^2 - b^2}{2\,a\,c} \text{ (using cosine rule)}$$

$$= \frac{6^2 + 3^2 - 5^2}{2 \times 6 \times 3}$$

$$= \frac{36 + 9 - 25}{36}$$

$$= \frac{20}{36}$$

$$= \frac{5}{9}$$

8.

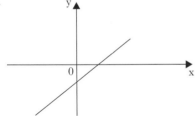

9. (*a*) P-G-A-N-E, P-G-E-A-N, P-G-E-N-A, P-G-N-A-E, P-G-N-E-A

A tree diagram showing the following routes:
P-G-A-N-E, P-G-E-AN, P-G-E-N-A, P-G-N-A-E, P-G-N-E-A

(*b*) Shortest distance, finishing at Newcastle, is 431 miles

10. $\dfrac{4}{5}$

MATHEMATICS INTERMEDIATE 2 UNITS 1, 2 AND APPLICATIONS PAPER 2 2011

1. $-9/10$

2. £147 900

3. (*a*) 106 cubic metres

(*b*) 17·4 metres

4. 25·1 square metres

5. (*a*) (i) $\bar{x} = 41$
    (ii) $s = 2\cdot1$

(*b*) Yes, with reasons covering both conditions

6. (*a*) $24x + 6y = 60$

(*b*) $20x + 10y = 40$

(*c*) 25 points

7. Finesave without payment protection

8. (*a*) 4 runners
(*b*) 6

9. £9·36

10. (*a*) = B4/12

(*b*) = SUM(D4:D8)

(*c*) £87 750

(*d*) £50 700, £46 200, so Paywell pays more

11. 21 centimetres

12. 25·1 millimetres

MATHEMATICS INTERMEDIATE 2 UNITS 1, 2 AND APPLICATIONS PAPER 1 2012 (NON-CALCULATOR)

1. £1 158 000 000 000

2. (a)

mark	frequency	cumulative frequency
5	2	2
6	5	7
7	6	13
8	11	24
9	9	33
10	2	35

   (b) (i) 8
       (ii) 7
       (iii) 9

   (c)

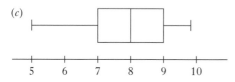

3. (a) A(0, 12)

   (b) C(3, 8)

4. 34°

5. (a) 20 160

   (b) The median, with reason. The reason must refer to the fact that the mean is affected by one very high attendance or that the median is closer to the majority of the attendances.

6. 1·7

7. 10 centimetres

8. (a) $(a + b)^2$

   (b) 10 000

9. (a) =D8*0·16

   (b) =G8*0·05

   (c) £53·37

10. 5 hours

MATHEMATICS INTERMEDIATE 2 UNITS 1, 2 AND APPLICATIONS PAPER 2 2012

1. 12.5 centimetres

2. $3x^3 + x^2 - 28x + 30$

3. 1022 mm^3

4. £25·92

5. (a) (i) 116
      (ii) 16·33

   (b) 1 and 4 (The total score is the same in both matches and in the first match the scores are more spread out.)

6. (a) $6x + 2y = 3148$

   (b) $5x + 3y = 3022$

   (c) Yes. The group has been overcharged by £10.

7.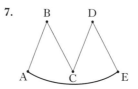

8. £1016·40

9. 1·32

10. 0·4

11. 20·5

12. 75·3 metres

13. No, 0·522 > 0·5

MATHEMATICS INTERMEDIATE 2 UNITS 1, 2 AND APPLICATIONS PAPER 1 2013 (NON-CALCULATOR)

1. $b(6a - 7c)$

2. $y = -\dfrac{4}{3}x + 4$

3. $6 \cdot 28$ cm

4. $x = 4, y = -2$

5. $121°$

6. (a) (i) $Q_2 = 35$
   (ii) $Q_1 = 22$
   (iii) $Q_3 = 39$

   (b)

   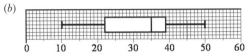

   (c) In general, the fourth year pupils spend more time on homework.
   There is less variation in the times spent on homework in fourth year than in first year.

7. (a)

   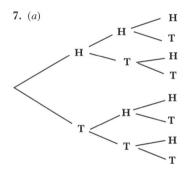

   (b) $\dfrac{3}{8}$

8. 90

9. (a) 1400 hours

   (b) 250 hours

MATHEMATICS INTERMEDIATE 2 UNITS 1, 2 AND APPLICATIONS PAPER 2 2013

1. $x^2 - 12x - 10$

2. 4 years because $307\,200 < 375\,000$

3. £1383·71

4.

[Pie chart: LIB DEM, CON 36°, OTHERS 36°, 54°, 126° SNP, 108° LABOUR]

5. £3704·60

6. A = £141·89 and B = £5

7. 30·6°

8. (a) (i) $\bar{x} = 82$
   (ii) $s = 3·54$

   (b) mean = 102
   standard deviation = 3·54

9. 14 cm

10. 7·6 metres

11. 85·4 cm

12. £6·50

13. (a)

Money collected (E)	Frequency
0·01 – 5·00	2
5·01 – 10·00	6
10·01 – 15·00	8
15·01 – 20·00	10
20·01 – 25·00	17
25·01 – 30·00	5
30·01 – 35·00	2

   (b) Yes, with evidence (e.g. work out the data in cumulative frequency column for the data in Diagram A and compare with the data in Diagram B).